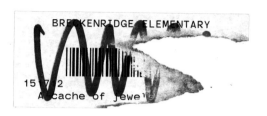

With

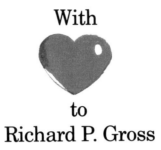

to
Richard P. Gross

Printed on recycled paper

J
428.1
HEL

RUTH HELLER

WORLD OF LANGUAGE

A CACHE OF JEWELS

and Other Collective Nouns

Written and illustrated by

RUTH HELLER

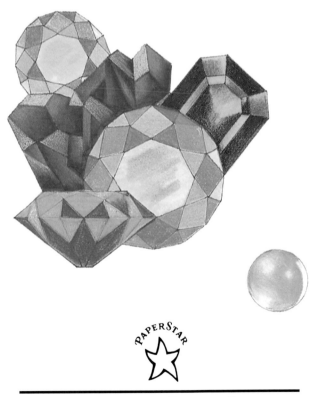

PAPERSTAR

The Putnam & Grosset Group

A word that means a collection of things,
like a

CACHE

of jewels
for the crowns of kings…

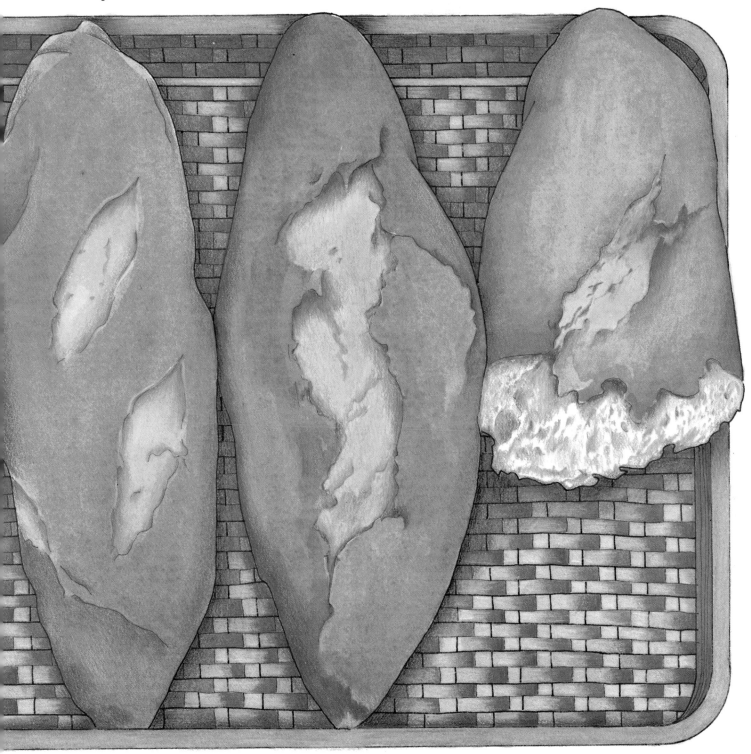

a **SCHOOL** of fish

a GAM of whales

a **FLEET** of ships
with
purple sails

a
CLUSTER
of
grapes

a
BEVY
of
beauties

.

all different
shapes

a **MUSTER** of peacocks

a
FLOCK
of
sheep

a
HOST
of
angels
fast
asleep

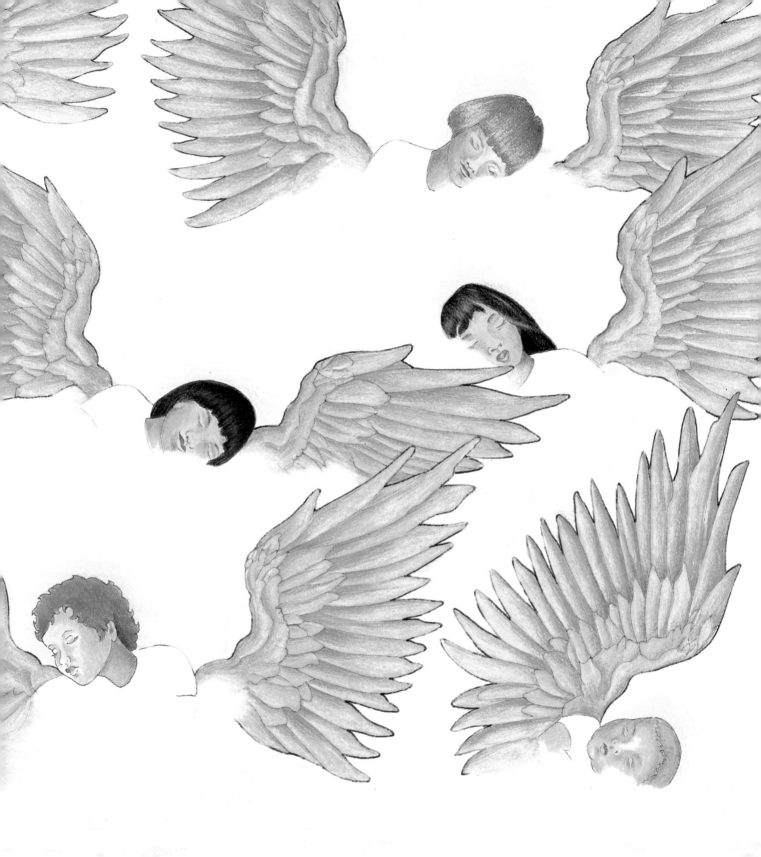

a **BOUQUET**
of flowers

a
SWARM
of
bees

a **KINDLE** of kittens
a
POD of peas

a **PARCEL** of
penguins

a
FOREST
of

trees

a
COVEN
of
witches
as
scary
as
these

a **DRIFT** of swans

a **CLUMP**
of reeds

a
BED
of
oysters

a
STRING
of
beads

a
BROOD
of
chicks

a
CLUTCH
of
eggs

a
LITTER
of puppies on wobbly legs

a
PRIDE
of lions

a
LOCK
of hair

an
ARMY
of ants
from
here to…

there....

About five hundred years ago
knights and ladies in the know
used only very special words
to describe their flocks or herds.

These words are used by us today,
but some were lost along the way,
and new ones have been added too.

I've included quite a few.

And there are more of these group terms
like   of bears
or   of worms
or   of turkeys
of snails
of leopards
of quails.

But nouns aren't all collective,
and if I'm to be effective,
I'll tell about the other nouns
and adjectives and verbs.

All of them are parts of speech.

What fun!
I'll write a book for each.

—*Ruth Heller*

<u>Note:</u> One collective noun can describe many groups, as in a **host** of angels, daffodils, monks, thoughts, or sparrows.

One group can be described by more than one collective noun as in a **gam** of whales, a **mob** of whales, a **pod** of whales, a **school** of whales, or a **run** of whales.